BIG
BOOK
of
crafts
& .
activities

LONDON, NEW YORK, MELBOURNE, MUNICH, AND DELHI

Editors James Mitchem, Cécile Landau
Senior Designer Wendy Bartlet
Designer Poppy Joslin
Photography Dave King
Additional editing Becky Alexander, Grace Redhead
Additional design Jess Bentall
Managing Editor Penny Smith
Managing Art Editor Marianne Markham
Art Director Jane Bull
Category Publisher Mary Ling
Producers Verity Powell, Sarah Tanner
Creative Technical Support Sonia Charbonnier
Jacket Designer Wendy Bartlet
DTP Designer Kavita Varma

This edition published in 2013
First published in Great Britain in 2013 by
Dorling Kindersley Limited, 80 Strand, London, WC2R 0RL
Penguin Group (UK)

Copyright© 2013 Dorling Kindersley Limited

10 9 8 7 6 5 4 3 2 1
001–185649–Aug/13

A CIP catalogue record for this book is available
from the British Library.

ISBN: 978-1-4093-3664-8

Printed and bound by Hung Hing, China.

Discover more at
www.dk.com

BIG
BOOK
of
crafts
&
activities

Contents

SAFETY

This book is packed with things to do – some are simple, while others are more tricky.
We hope you enjoy this book, but please be sensible and safe. Only attempt anything
dangerous such as cooking or cutting under the supervision of an adult .

The authors and publisher cannot take responsibility for the outcome, injury, loss, damage,
or mess that occurs as a result of you attempting the activities in this book. Tell an adult
before you do any of them, carefully read all the instructions, and seek help when you need it.

Make a pinboard

You will need
- Cotton fabric
- Polyester wadding
- Cork pinboard
- Staple gun and staples
- Ribbon • Tape
- Drawing pins

Pinboards are great for collecting your favourite odds and ends: photos, sketches, notes – anything you like! The best part is picking your fabric and making your pinboard look beautiful.

The fabric needs to go at the bottom

The wadding goes between the board and fabric

The board needs to be right in the centre

1. In order, put the fabric, the wadding, and the pinboard down on a surface. Make sure the pinboard goes with the cork side face down.

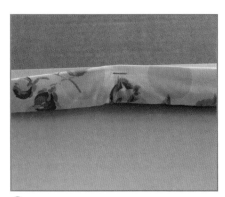

2. Fold the wadding and fabric up at one side and get an adult to staple it the middle. Do this for all four sides, making sure it's pulled tight.

3. For the corners, tuck one side of the fabric down into the other and fold the other side up as shown. Make sure it's nice and neat.

4. Once you've tucked in the corner neatly, get an adult to staple it in place on both sides. Do this for the other corners too.

You can make the ribbon run like this too

Use coloured pins that match your fabric

5. Spread strips of ribbon across the front diagonally and tape them in place. Turn the board over and get an adult to staple the ribbon to it.

6. Remove the tape and lay more ribbon across to create a pattern. Tape in place each time, and get an adult to staple it to the back.

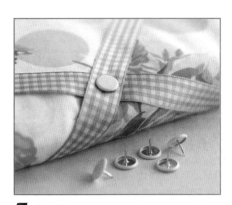

7. Push in drawing pins where the pieces of ribbon meet to keep them in place. Now it's time to add stuff to your pinboard.

Pretty hangers

Pretty clothes belong on a pretty hanger. The problem is that most hangers are boring. Luckily you can decorate these hangers so they look as good as your clothes!

You will need

• Wooden hangers
• Paper • Pencil
• Felt • Pins
• Polyester wadding
• Needle and thread

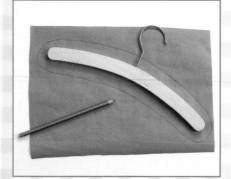

1. Lay a wooden hanger out on a piece of paper and draw around it, leaving a gap of about 2.5cm (1in) all round.

2. Carefully cut the shape out to create a template. You can use this template to decorate as many hangers as you want.

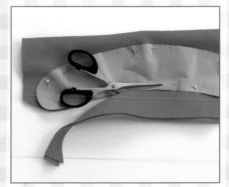

3. Fold a piece of felt in half and pin the template to it. Cut around it so that you have two identical pieces of felt. Then take out the pins.

4. Cut out a bit of wadding that is smaller than the felt but bigger than the hanger. Lay it on top of the felt, then put the hanger on top.

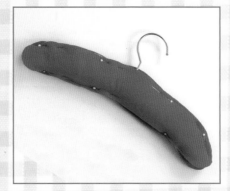

5. Put another strip of wadding and the other piece of felt on top of the hanger. Attach pins along the edges to keep it all in place.

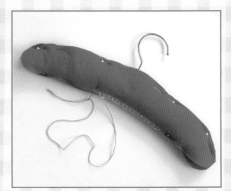

6. Use the needle and thread to stitch the felt together. Ask an adult help you with this. Remove the pins and decorate!

Cut flowers out of felt scraps and glue or stitch them on to your hanger

Furniture makeover

When you're in the process of giving your bedroom a makeover, a few posters will only go so far. If you have old furniture, you can give it a new lease of life with paint and decorations (if your parents agree!).

You will need
- Old furniture
- Sandpaper
- Undercoat paint
- Satinwood paint
- Ribbons, glue, and trim
- Hair clips

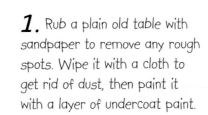

1. Rub a plain old table with sandpaper to remove any rough spots. Wipe it with a cloth to get rid of dust, then paint it with a layer of undercoat paint.

2. Once the undercoat paint has dried, paint the table in your favourite colours using satinwood paint and leave to dry. Try not to leave any drips.

1. Rub the chair with sandpaper as above and apply a layer of undercoat paint. Make sure you cover the chair completely, painting behind the legs too.

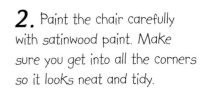

2. Paint the chair carefully with satinwood paint. Make sure you get into all the corners so it looks neat and tidy.

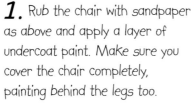

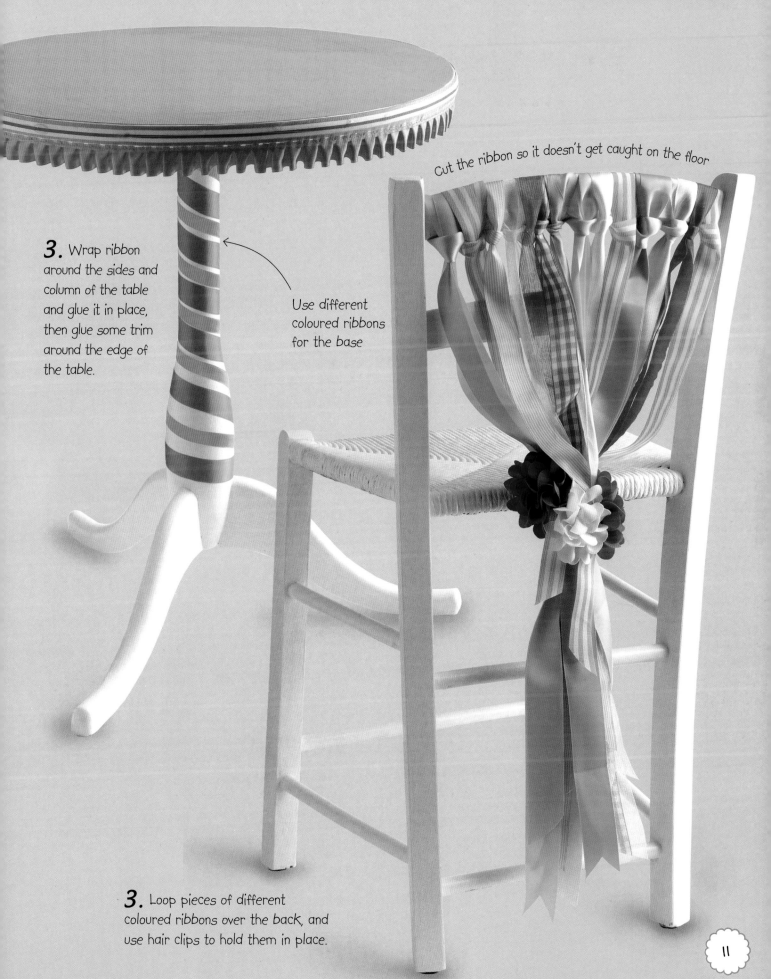

Cut the ribbon so it doesn't get caught on the floor

3. Wrap ribbon around the sides and column of the table and glue it in place, then glue some trim around the edge of the table.

Use different coloured ribbons for the base

3. Loop pieces of different coloured ribbons over the back, and use hair clips to hold them in place.

More furniture

Chairs and tables are one thing, but decorating a bedside table or chest of drawers will really breathe new life into your bedroom. Here's a suggestion for how to do it.

You will need
- Furniture • Sandpaper
- Undercoat paint
- Satinwood paint
- Card • Fabric • Stapler
- Ribbon

1. Unscrew any knobs. Rub the furniture with sandpaper, then paint with the undercoat, then satinwood paint.

2. Once the paint has dried, measure the side panel with a ruler and cut out a piece of card the exact same size.

3. Lay the card on top of your chosen fabric. Turn over the edges and either glue down or staple in place.

4. Glue the card to the side of the cupboard and then repeat this for the other side and the front.

5. Cut out a circle of fabric to cover the knob. Put the knob in the middle of the fabric. Scrunch it around the knob.

6. Tie the fabric in place with narrow ribbon. Trim off any excess fabric then screw the knob back on.

Choose fabric and paint that go together: this paint matches some of the yellow petals in the pattern

Colourful fabric makes your furniture unique

Use enough ribbon so that it hangs down and looks stylish

13

Custom cushions

Adding a fabric picture to a plain old cushion is a great way to make it stand out. Here's how to make one with a strawberry motif – but you can use any shape or design you like.

You will need
- Pencil and paper
- Bondaweb • Iron • Fabric
- Cushion cover
- Needle and thread

1. Neatly draw your strawberry onto paper and place the bondaweb on top. Trace around the strawberry and cut it out.

2. Ask an adult to iron the bondaweb shapes onto coloured fabric. Use red for the strawberry and green for the leaves.

3. Cut around the fabric and bondaweb carefully. Try to be as neat as you can.

4. Lay your design with the bondaweb side face down on the cushion cover. Get an adult to iron over the shapes.

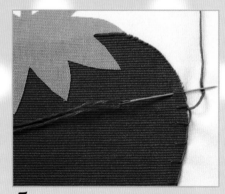

5. Use the needle and thread to sew around your strawberry to help keep it in place.

6. Sew green thread around the leaves and stalk. Use either white or yellow thread on the strawberry to make pips.

Why not decorate more cushions? Try a raspberry picture or a red flower and make a set.

Pamper day

Which one is your favourite?

The next time you want to pamper yourself, treat yourself and your friends to a home spa day with facemasks and smoothies.

Fruity smoothies are a delicious, healthy treat. To make them, all you do is whizz the ingredients together in a blender. Add a few ice cubes if you like, and serve with a few fresh berries on top.

Blackberry and Blueberry

Ingredients
• 60g (2oz) blackberries
• 60g (2oz) strawberries
• 30g (1oz) blueberries
• ¼ banana
• 4 tbsp blueberry yoghurt
• 2 tsp honey

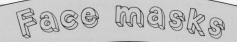

Face masks

Yoghurt and egg whites
Crack two eggs and get rid of the yolks. Put the egg whites in a bowl and add 2 tbsp of plain yoghurt (don't use the flavoured stuff!) Mix together until smooth.

Banana and honey
Mash a banana with 1 tbsp of honey and a drop of orange juice. Mix until smooth.

Avocado and honey
Mash an avocado and ½ cup of honey in a bowl. Mix together until smooth.

Facemasks are a great way to refresh your skin. All you need are a few ingredients from home such as bananas and honey! Apply the mask to your face and rinse it off with warm water after 10 minutes.

Strawberry and Honey

Ingredients
• 100g (3½oz) strawberries
• ¼ banana
• 2 tsp honey
• 6 tbsp strawberry yoghurt

Tropical Banana

Ingredients
• 1 mango, chopped
• ¼ banana
• 30g (1oz) pineapple chunks
• 6 tbsp pineapple juice
• 4 tbsp vanilla yoghurt

Banana Caramel

Drizzle caramel on top!

Ingredients
• 2½ tbsp dulche de leche
• 100ml (3½fl oz) milk
• 1 banana
• 4 tbsp plain yoghurt

Bath bombs

A lot of people add bubbles to their baths to make them more fun. But if you drop a bath bomb into the tub instead, it'll fizz about, adding colour and a lovely smell to your bath. Even better than bubbles!

You will need

- 200g (7oz) bicarbonate of soda
- 100g (3½oz) citric acid
- Food colouring
- 2 tbsp olive oil

- Scented oil
- Spray bottle
- Witch hazel
- Plastic moulds
- Sprinkles or cake decorations

1. Pour the bicarbonate of soda and the citric acid into a large mixing bowl.

2. Add a few teaspoons (or drops) of food colouring and stir it in. Use whichever colours you like.

3. Add the olive oil. Try to sprinkle it over the surface, rather than pour it all in the middle.

4. Then add a few drops of your favourite scented oil. Lavender or vanilla work really well.

5. Mix everything together with your hands. Try to break up any big lumps you find.

6. Use the mist feature on the spray bottle to add a few squirts of witch hazel into the mixture.

Try lemon and strawberry scented oils too

7. Mix everything together until it feels like damp sand. If it's too dry, add a little more witch hazel.

8. Press the mixture into the plastic moulds. Add sprinkles or cake decorations to the bath bombs.

9. Squeeze the moulds shut and leave your bath bombs to harden for five hours. Is it bath time yet?

19

Button jewellery

Buttons are a cheap and easy way of making funky custom jewellery. So grab some colourful buttons and get started with this hair clip, bracelet, and brooch. Can you think of anything else to make?

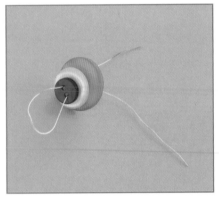

1. Stack buttons together with the smallest one on top. Loop craft wire through the button holes.

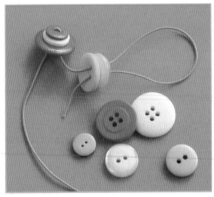

1. Stack a few buttons together and thread elastic string through the holes. Repeat with more buttons.

1. Turn a big button upside down and get an adult to glue small buttons around the edge using a glue gun.

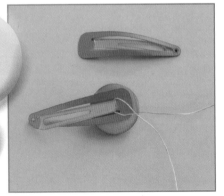

2. Wrap the wire around the top of the hair clip and pull it tight. Tie it in a knot and cut off the excess.

2. Repeat this until you have a circle, making sure the buttons overlap. Tie the ends of the string together.

2. Leave it to dry and turn it over. Get an adult to glue a brooch pin to the back or sew it to anything you like.

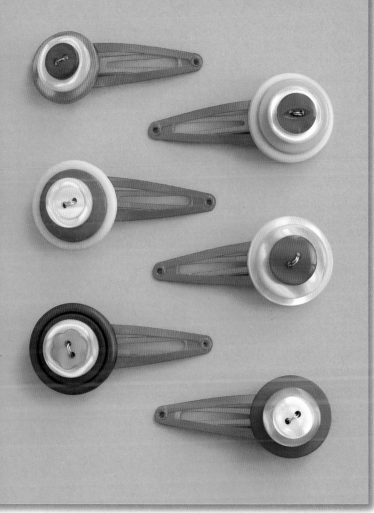

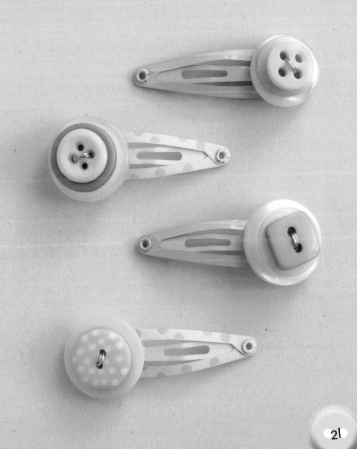

Customize shoes

Plain canvas shoes are always fashionable, but if you decorate them, not only will they look even cooler, but they'll be totally one of a kind!

You will need
- Canvas shoes
- All-purpose glue
- Sequins and decorations
- Ribbon
- Clear tape
- Fabric pens

1. Choose a pair of shoes to decorate. If you're using an old pair, make sure to give them a good clean first. Take out the laces.

2. Glue the sequins or decorations to the toe of the shoes. Make a pattern using different colours.

3. Glue more sequins along the seam under the loops that the laces go through. Leave a gap between each one.

4. Roll up the ends of the ribbon and wrap a piece of tape around the ends to help you thread your new laces.

Or, try this...

Customize!

It's up to you how you want your shoes to look. You can use fabric pens to sketch your own design, or get really creative with decorations.

Try either matching or different coloured ribbon for the laces

Recycled pom-poms

Making pom-poms takes a bit of patience, but they're a lot of fun, and make great decorations. These are made with old plastic bags so are great recycling and free to make!

You will need
- Cardboard
- Scissors
- Plastic bags
- String

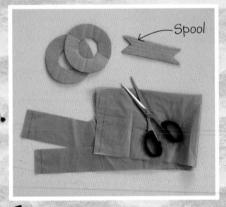

1. Cut two 7.5cm (3in) circles out of cardboard, and cut holes in the middle. Cut a small pice of cardboard to use as a spool, as shown.

Spool

2. Lay one of your plastic bags on its side. Cut off the base and the handles, and smooth out any wrinkles.

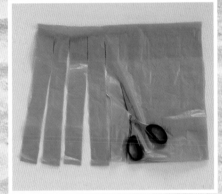

3. From the bottom of the bag, make cuts up to 2.5cm (1in) from the top, leaving 2.5cm (1in) gaps between the cuts.

4. Do the same from the top, making the cuts in between the strips you made already. Like before, leave a 2.5cm (1in) gap at the bottom.

5. Cut along the bottom and top of the bag, leaving the top right corner untouched. You'll be left with one long strip. Wrap it around the spool.

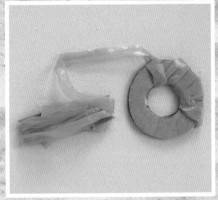

6. Put the two rings together and wrap the plastic around them until you run out. Use the spool to help thread the plastic through the hole.

Flip flops

You can use your pom-poms to decorate clothes, shoes, or bags. Dancers and cheerleaders can use them to shake in their routines. What will you do with yours?

7. Cut the plastic all the way around the outside edge of the cardboard rings. Don't cut all the way through to the middle.

8. Wrap string between the rings and pull it tight. Tie a tight knot. The string should squeeze the plastic into the gap in the ring.

9. Cut or pull off the cardboard rings. Fluff the pom-pom and trim off any excess string.

Grow your own veg

Growing your own fruit and vegetables isn't very hard. With a little patience and tender care, you'll have fresh lettuce, carrots, tomatoes, and potatoes to use in your recipes.

Lettuce

Fill small pots with seed compost and use a pencil to make 1cm (½in) trenches. Sprinkle lettuce seeds into the trenches and cover them in soil. Water the seeds regularly and after about 10 weeks you will have lettuce to harvest!

You will need

- Small pots
- Seed compost
- Lettuce, carrot, and tomato seeds
- Deep pots
- Soil-based compost
- Egg cartons • Canes
- Seed potatoes

It's very important to wash anything you grow before you eat it

Do you like red or green lettuce?

Carrots

Fill a deep pot with soil-based compost and fill a 1cm (½in) trench with carrot seeds. Cover them with soil and water regularly. After about two weeks, small seedlings should have grown. If the pot is crowded, pick some out.

Tomatoes

Cut an egg carton in half. Fill it with soil and push a few tomato seeds into each egg cup. Water them regularly and after about two weeks transfer any seedlings to their own pots. Stick a cane into the soil next to each plant and tie the stem to it as it grows.

Carrots take about 12 weeks to grow

It will be 20 weeks before you can pick your tomatoes

Potatoes

Plant seed potatoes in holes 15cm (6in) deep, and 30cm (12in) apart in the ground. Make sure they are in a place that gets a lot of light. Water regularly and after 20 weeks, dig up one of the plants to see if the potatoes are ready.

Strawberry boots

Did you know that you can grow delicious strawberries in your back garden? Planting them in a pot is fine, but where's the fun in that? A pair of old wellington boots works just as well, and looks much better.

You will need
- Wellington boots
- Gravel
- Six strawberry plants
- Soil • Eggshells
- Petroleum jelly

1. Ask an adult to cut a hole on each side of the boots (one higher than the other). Each hole should be about the size of the plant's root ball.

2. Put a little gravel in the bottom of the boots to allow for drainage. Add enough soil so that it's level with the first hole in the side.

3. Push a plant sideways into the first hole, then fill the boot with more soil. When you reach the second hole, put in the second plant.

4. Place a third plant into the top of the boot. Level off the soil and press down firmly. Repeat this with the other boot. Water both boots well.

5. Cover the surface of the boots with broken eggshells to keep slugs off. Feed the plants with tomato food every week.

6. Rub petroleum jelly over the sides of the boots to keep the slugs and snails away. Make sure to water your plants regularly.

It will take about 12 weeks for your plants to produce fruit

29

When each sunflower has opened, use a pencil to pick out the middle to make a face

Sunflower people

It will take a while, but if you're looking for something fun to do in the summer, why not grow sunflower people? They'll look great in any garden.

You will need
- Paint tins with holes in the bottom
- Polythene bags with holes in the bottom
- Gravel • Soil
- Sunflower seeds

1. Decorate the paint tins and line them with the bags. Put a layer of gravel in the bottom, then fill them with soil and water generously.

2. Make two holes 1cm (½in) deep in each pots and sow a seed into each one. Cover the seeds with soil, then cover each tin with a bag.

3. Put the tins in sunlight and water the plants little but often. When leaves appear, take off the bag and remove the smallest plant.

4. It will take about 10 weeks for the flowers to grow. Keep watering the plants, and remove any extra sunflower heads that may appear.

Sleepover games

Hosting a sleepover but stuck for things to do? There's a bundle of great games you can play – take your pick!

Makeover madness

Place make-up in the centre of a circle. On the count of three everyone grabs a selection and gets into pairs. One person puts a blindfold on (a scarf will do) and attempts to apply make-up to their partner. Now swap!

Spin the polish

Get everyone to bring nail polish and put it in a basket. Roll a dice – this will be the number of nails to be painted. Select a nail colour and spin the bottle. Who does the cap point to? Paint the correct number of her nails in the selected colour.

Dance idols

Split everybody into small teams and make up dances to your favourite music. Draw some scorecards onto paper and get the other teams to watch and judge – will you have the X-factor?

Two truths and a lie

Everybody has to think up two truths and a lie about themselves. Take it in turns to present them to the others and see if they can discover which is the lie – it'll be harder than you think! Find some sweets for the winners, or treat them to a nail-painting session.

Movie trivia

Before the sleepover, pick a movie to watch and make up trivia questions about it. Once your friends arrive, watch the movie. When it's finished, have a contest to see who can come up with the most correct answers.

Grab that spoon!

Put as many spoons as players, minus one, on a table and deal out cards. The dealer discards a card, then the player on their left picks it up and discards one of theirs. If you match four cards you take a spoon. Last person to get a spoon loses!

Scary stories

Turn out all the lights and get everybody to sit in a circle. Take turns telling your scariest ghost stories. Who's the biggest scaredy cat?

Smoothie sensation

You'll need a blender, natural yoghurt, and bowls of different fruits, such as strawberries, blueberries, and bananas. Whizz the different fruits with the yoghurt – which smoothie is the nicest?

33

Use pink and white marshmallows

Hot chocolate

Pour the milk into a saucepan and grate in the chocolate. Mix it together over a medium heat for about four minutes, or until the chocolate has dissolved. Add a few drops of flavouring, then pour the hot chocolate into mugs. Add marshmallows, sprinkle over cocoa powder, and serve!

Ingredients
- 600ml (1pt) milk
- 100g (3½oz) chocolate
- Mint, orange, or vanilla extract
- Marshmallows
- Cocoa powder

Midnight feast

25 mins

One of the best parts of a sleepover is the midnight feast. The next time your friends are over, spoil yourselves rotten with these cookies and hot chocolate.

Ingredients

- 100g (3½oz) butter, softened
- 100g (3½oz) brown sugar
- 1 medium egg, beaten
- 100g (3½oz) plain flour
- 1 tbsp cocoa powder
- 50g (1¾oz) milk chocolate, chopped
- 50g (1¾oz) white chocolate, chopped
- ½ tsp baking powder
- 25g (1oz) mini marshmallows

Makes 14

1. Preheat the oven to 180°C (375°F). Line baking trays with *baking* paper. Cream the butter and sugar together in a mixing bowl.

2. Beat the egg into the mixture, and stir in the flour, cocoa powder, half of both types of chocolate, and the baking powder.

3. Place dessert-sized spoons of mixture onto the trays. Leave a space between each one. Flatten with the spoon and *bake* for 5 minutes.

4. Remove the cookies. Press the rest of the chocolate and the marshmallows on top. Bake for 10 minutes, until crisp around the edges.

Banana pancakes

The perfect way to finish a sleepover is cooking breakfast the morning after. These American-style banana pancakes are great because as well as being delicious, they're really fun to flip!

Ingredients

- 2 tbsp caster sugar
- 100g (3½oz) self-raising flour
- 45g (1½oz) self-raising wholemeal flour
- 150ml (5fl oz) milk
- 1 egg • 2 ripe bananas
- Butter, for frying

Makes 12

1. Sift the sugar and both types of flour into a bowl. Mix them together. Make a well in the centre.

2. Pour the milk into a measuring jug and crack the egg into it. Beat it with a fork until it's all mixed together.

3. Pour the egg and milk into the well you made in the flour. Beat the mixture with a spoon until creamy.

4. Leave the mixture for about 30 minutes. Mash the bananas, then stir them into the pancake mixture.

5. Heat a knob of butter in a pan. Add three small ladlefuls of batter, each one about 7.5cm (3in) across.

6. Cook the pancakes for two minutes. Flip them over and cook for another two minutes.

Flipping crêpes

American-style pancakes are easy to flip *because* they're thick. But thin French crêpes are harder. The trick is to tilt the mixture so it covers the *base* of the pan. After a minute, lift the edges with a spatula to loosen them, then flip the pancake in the air. Get an adult to show you how – the last thing you want is pancake on the ceiling!

Drizzle your pancakes in yummy maple syrup!

Blueberries and raspberries are delicious with pancakes

Friendship bracelets

Making a friendship bracelet is a great way to show somebody that they're important to you. It's a bonus that they're fashionable and easy to make as well.

You will need
• Suede twine or embroidery thread
• Beads

Easy

1. Take two pieces of twine about the length of your arm. Make a loop in one and lay it flat, then wrap the second piece around it as shown.

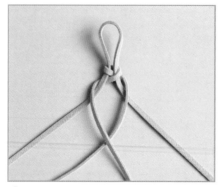

2. Cross the two ends of the second thread over each other. Wrap them around the outside of the first thread and pull tight.

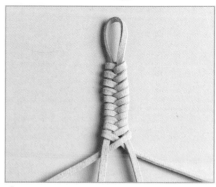

3. Repeat this – crossing the ends over each other and going around the first thread – until your bracelet is long enough. Trim off the ends.

Hard

1. Line up six lengths of different coloured thread each about as long as your arm. Knot them together near the top.

2. Take the first coloured thread and loop it over then under the second strand and pull it tight. Repeat this to create a double knot.

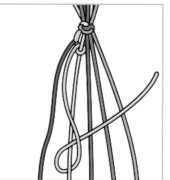

3. Do this again over the next thread, then the next until the first piece has moved all the way to the right side.

4. Repeat this process with the second thread, and then carry on until the bracelet is long enough. Knot it together and trim off the ends.

Once you're good at this, you can try threading beads in

Make a couple of different patterns by swirling and whirling the paint colours!

Marbled paper

You can use marbled paper to decorate all sorts of things. You can wrap things in it, use it as a background, or write on it. Better still, it's cheap and very easy to make.

You will need
- Paint pots and oil paints
- Turpentine
- Disposable baking tray
- Cocktail sticks
- Paper
- Newspaper

1. Mix a blob of paint with four caps of turpentine. Fill the tray with 2.5cm (1in) of water and add a few spoonfuls of the paint mixture.

2. Add a second colour paint mixture, and swish and swirl it around with a cocktail stick to make an interesting pattern.

3. Lay a sheet of paper on the surface of the water to absorb some of the paint.

4. Pick the paper up by the corners and lift it out of the tray. Lay it on newspaper to dry.

Piñata party

Piñatas are a tradition at birthdays and festivals in Mexico. They're stuffed with sweets and toys and hung from trees. Children take turns bashing them open to get to the sweets! The next time you're celebrating something, why not make this fluffy owl piñata?

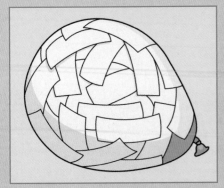

1. Inflate and tie the balloon. Glue strips of newspaper to the balloon, leaving a gap at the bottom where the knot is.

2. Let it dry, and then repeat with two more layers. Pop the balloon with a pin and trim away the knot so you are left with a shell.

3. Cut the tissue paper into strips and make cuts along the edge to create fringing. Glue layers of paper to the shell, starting from the bottom.

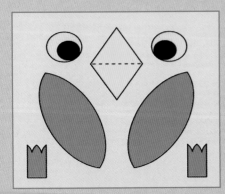

4. Cut out eyes, a beak, feet, and wings from the card and glue them to the shell. Use more tissue paper to decorate the rest of the owl.

5. Make two holes in the top of the piñata with a pencil. Loop a length of string through one hole and out the other. Tie it together.

6. Fill the owl with sweets and toys. Cut a piece of card big enough to cover the hole, and use tape to keep it in place.

Piñata time!

Whack it!

Hang the piñata from a tree. Players then put on a blindfold (a scarf is fine) and take turns swinging at the piñata with a stick. When the sweets spill out, it's a free-for-all! Grab some before they're gone!

This will make a brilliant birthday present for your friends!

Customize your diary

You will need
- Diary
- Coloured felt
- Needle and thread
- Buttons • Glue
- Coloured elastic
- Mini peg
- Wooden toggle

Writing a diary is a great way of keeping a record of the things you've done, and it's really fun to look back each year. If your diary looks a bit plain, why not customize it with this cute bird design?

1. Choose a diary to decorate. You can use a brand new one, or if you already have one you can use that.

2. Cut out the shape of a bird from felt. Cut out a smaller version for a wing. Sew a border around the bird, and then sew on the wing.

3. Sew on a button for an eye, and glue your bird to your diary. Make legs from elastic and glue them under the bird. Use a mini peg as a beak.

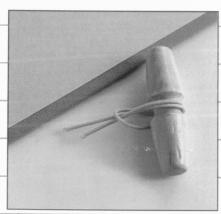

4. Make a loop in a piece of elastic and wrap it around the toggle. Thread the ends back through the loop, securing it in place.

5. Open the diary and position the toggle so that the elastic sits inside the front cover, as shown. Cut out a piece of felt big enough to cover it.

6. Glue the elastic and felt to the inside of the front cover. Once it has dried, decorate your diary with beads, buttons, and sequins.

45

If you're painting your creatures, it's easier to do it before you glue

Pebble creatures

You can make cool creatures out of almost anything – even pebbles! Next time you're at the beach or the park look for pebbles in a variety of colours, patterns, and sizes.

You will need

- Pebbles
- Strong glue
- Googly eyes
- Felt
- Acrylic paint

1. Gather the things you will need and decide which animals you're going to make. Give the pebbles a wash to get any dirt off.

2. Glue pebbles in a line to make a caterpillar. It's easy to make and will get you used to glueing pebbles together.

3. For a mouse, add googly eyes. To make ears, cut out pieces of felt, squeeze one end together, and glue in place.

4. Once the glue has dried, try making other creatures. Look at your stones carefully. Which animals do they remind you of?

Choose your favourite colours to decorate your frame

Make sure you can still see the picture!

Customize your frames

Customize your frames

It's great to display pictures of your friends, family, holidays, and pets, but some photo frames can look a bit dull. Here are ideas to jazz them up.

You will need
- Photo frames
- Acrylic paints
- Mini pom-poms, fur trim, beads, glitter, felt, and stickers
- Glue or a glue gun

1. If you have coloured frames, skip to step 2. Otherwise, get some plain frames and take the backing and glass out. Paint the frames with different coloured acrylic paints (you might need two coats). Once the frames are dry put the back and glass in again.

2. Squeeze glue on the frame or ask an adult to put spots of glue on the frame with a glue gun. Stick on the pom-poms.

3. Decide how you want to decorate your frames. Experiment with materials such as fur trim, beads, glitter, felt, or stickers.

Ice lollies

Looking for fun and fancy ways to cool down during the summer heat? With these fab lollies and icy bowl you'll be chilling out in no time.

Serves 4

1. Peel, the peaches and remove the stones. Chop the peaches into chunks.

2. Put the peaches, orange juice, and sugar into a blender and mix everything until smooth.

3. Pour the mixture into lolly moulds. Add a few pieces of tinned fruit salad for a delicious surprise!

4. Push the lolly sticks into the moulds and put them in the freezer for about 5 hours.

Fruit salad chunks make the lollies even tastier!

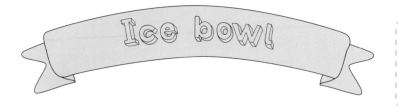

Ice bowl

You will need

• Two plastic bowls • Fruit slices and leaves • Tape

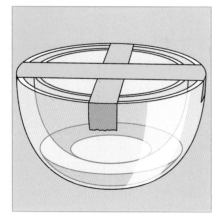

1. Fill a bowl with about 2.5cm (1in) of water and put it in the freezer. Once it's solid, put a smaller bowl on top of the ice, and tape it in place.

2. Pour water into the gap between the two bowls. Add decorations such as fruit slices and leaves and use a fork to spread them around.

3. Put the bowls in the freezer for 10 hours. Remove the tape and turn the bowl upside down so that your ice bowl slides out, ready to use!

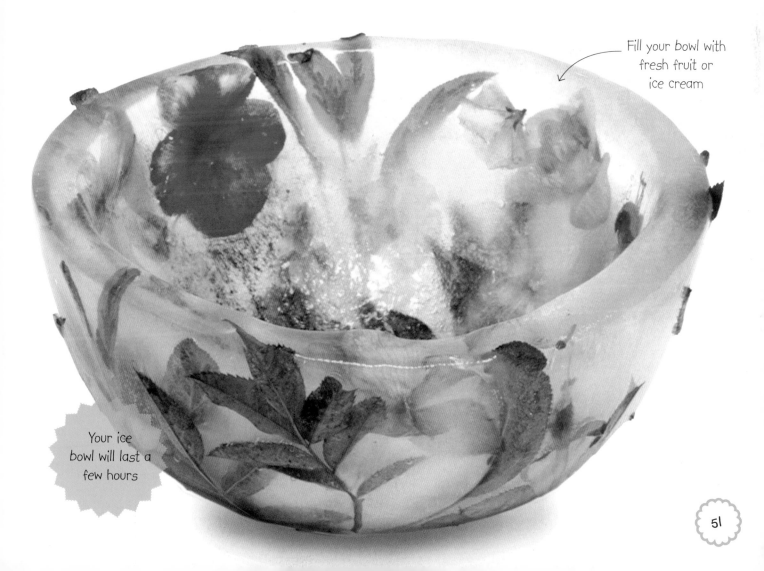

Fill your bowl with fresh fruit or ice cream

Your ice bowl will last a few hours

51

Picnic brownies

If you're going on a picnic, you'll need something sweet to have after your sandwiches. Make these brownies and lemonade ahead of time and pack them in your picnic basket for an afternoon treat.

Ingredients

- 85g (3oz) plain chocolate
- 150g (5½oz) unsalted butter • ½ tsp salt
- 125g (4½oz) plain flour • ½ tsp baking powder • 15g (½oz) cocoa powder
- 2 eggs • 300g (10oz) brown sugar
- 1 tsp vanilla extract
- 100g (3½oz) chopped pecan nuts

Makes 12

1. Preheat the oven to 180°C (350°F). Put the chocolate and butter in a pan over a low heat. Stir until melted.

2. Pour the mixture into a bowl. Sieve in the salt, flour, baking powder, and cocoa powder, and mix together.

3. In another bowl, mix the eggs, sugar, and vanilla extract. Stir in the chocolate mixture and pecans.

4. Line a baking tin with baking paper. Pour the mixture into the tin and smooth it out. Bake for 25 minutes. Leave it to cool, then cut into squares.

Pink lemonade

A cold glass of pink lemonade is the perfect refreshment on a hot summer's day, and goes beautifully with those rich brownies!

1. Peel the zest from the lemons with a potato peeler, and squeeze the juice into a heatproof jug.

2. Add the lemon zest and sugar, then pour in the boiling water. Stir it together until the sugar has dissolved.

3. Leave it to cool, then strain the lemonade into a serving jug. Add the cranberry juice, cold water, and ice. Serve with sliced lemon.

Ingredients

- 4 unwaxed lemons
- 100g (3½oz) caster sugar
- 600ml (!pt) boiling water
- 200ml (7fl oz) cranberry juice
- 200ml (7fl oz) cold water
- Ice
- Lemon slices

Summer salads

Here are four tasty salads that are perfect as a snack, or in a picnic basket. Perfect for sharing – you can all try a little of each one!

Chicken pasta salad

Serves 4

Ingredients

- 100g (3½oz) dried pasta bows
- 350g (12oz) cooked chicken breast, diced
- 2 spring onions, chopped
- ½ tomato, diced
- Juice of ½ lemon
- 3 tbsp yoghurt
- 2 tbsp sweetcorn
- 3 tbsp mayonnaise
- 2 tbsp chopped dill

Serve the pasta in little plastic cups

Cook the pasta in a saucepan of boiling water for 10 minutes, then drain and rinse it under cold water. Place the cooked pasta in a large bowl and mix in the rest of the ingredients. Keep refrigerated until ready to serve.

For a vegetarian version, leave out the chicken and add extra vegetables such as green beans

Potato salad

Ingredients

• 500g (1lb 2oz) baby new potatoes
• 3 tbsp crème fraîche
• 3 tbsp yoghurt

Wash the potatoes and cut them in half. Boil them in a saucepan for 12-15 minutes. While they cool, mix the crème fraîche and yoghurt in a bowl. Add this to the potatoes and stir everything together. Keep refrigerated until ready to serve.

Serves 4

Sprinkle chives on top to decorate

Picnic salad

Ingredients

• ½ cucumber, cut into chunks
• ½ red onion, sliced
• 12 cherry tomatoes, cut into quarters
• 2 wholemeal pitta breads
• 1 tbsp olive oil
• 150g (5½oz) feta cheese

Put the cucumber, onion, and tomatoes into a large bowl. Toast the pitta bread and cut into small pieces. Add them to the salad. Sprinkle on the olive oil. Toss the salad together. Scatter the feta on top, and refrigerate until ready.

Serves 4

Green salad

Ingredients

• 100g (3½oz) green beans
• 100g (3½oz) broccoli
• 100g (3½oz) fresh peas
• 150g (5½oz) mixed leaves (rocket, baby spinach etc.)

Pour on your favourite salad dressing

Steam the green beans for two minutes, then add the broccoli and peas and steam for three more. Put the vegetables on top of the mixed leaves on a large plate, ready to serve.

Serves 4

Make a kite

Whether you're at the beach or the park, flying a kite is a great way to have fun in the summer. Using things you have at home, you can make your own kite that will be prettier than the rest!

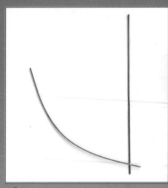

1. Soak the canes overnight to make them flexible. Wrap thread around two canes 5cm (2in) from the ends, as shown.

2. Bend one of the canes towards the middle and secure it in place with the thread. Make sure it's very tight.

3. Finish the frame by attaching a cane to the other side. Then two more that link them to the top, as shown.

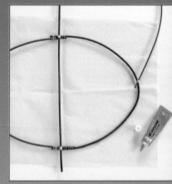

4. Put glue onto the bottom half of your frame. Lay the frame onto tissue paper, with the glue side down.

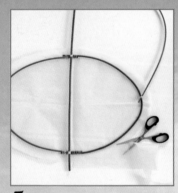

5. Once the glue has dried, cut around the shape of the frame, leaving a border of about 5cm (2in).

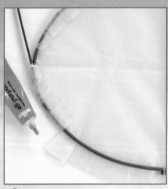

6. Cut the border into small strips and then fold them over the cane and glue them in place.

7. Repeat this with another piece of tissue paper. Where the two pieces meet, trim the paper and glue to the cane.

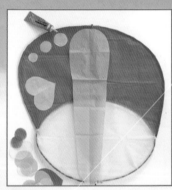

8. Turn the kite over. Cut out a strip of tissue paper for the body and glue it in place. Add other pieces to decorate.

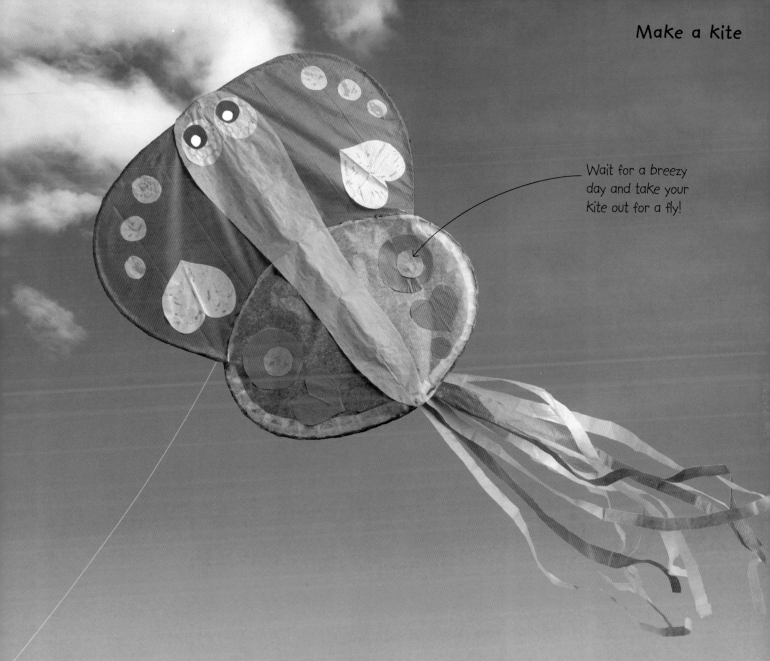

Wait for a breezy
day and take your
kite out for a fly!

9. Cut and fold five long
strips of tissue paper to
make streamers. Line the
ends up and staple together.

10. Glue the streamers to
the bottom of the kite. Cut
two lengths of kite string 5cm
(2in) longer than your kite.

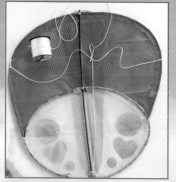

11. Tie one length around the
cane at the bottom, and the
other to each side, making a
small hole in the tissue paper.

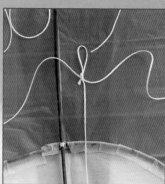

12. Tie the bottom string to
the horizontal one and make
a loop. Thread the rest of the
kite string through the loop.

Toffee popcorn

Warm, homemade popcorn is a delicious treat, and much tastier than the stuff you buy in the shops. You can have it at any get together, but it's especially good for a movie night. And for afterwards, try these chocolately banana bites.

Ingredients
- 2 tbsp corn oil
- 100g (3½oz) popping corn
- 50g (1¾oz) butter
- 50g (1¾oz) soft brown sugar
- 75ml (2½fl oz) golden syrup

1. Put the oil into a saucepan on a medium heat. Add the corn and put the lid on. Get an adult to shake the pan and let it pop away for a while.

2. In another pan, stir the butter, sugar, and syrup over a medium heat until it has melted into a toffee sauce.

3. When the popcorn is ready, put it into a large bowl and coat it with the sauce. Mix it together with a spoon, let it cool down, and eat!

You know your corn is nearly ready when the pops are a few seconds apart

Banana bites

Makes 15

1. Break the chocolate into a bowl and put it over a pan of warm water. Stir the chocolate until it's melted.

2. Chop the bananas into even-sized chunks. Push a straw through the centre of each one and put them on a plate.

Why not try chocolate sprinkles?

Coconut flakes work too

You will need
• 150g (5½oz) chocolate
• 2-3 bananas
• Straws
• Hundreds and thousands

3. Spoon the chocolate over the bananas and coat them evenly. Roll in hundreds and thousands then leave in the fridge to set.

Have fun icing and decorating your cupcakes – use sprinkles, and sweets

Cupcake heaven

30 mins

These cupcakes are perfect for a tea party. Once they are baked, get creative and decorate them with icing and sweets. Try not to eat them straightaway!

Ingredients

- 150g (5½oz) butter, softened
- 150g (5½oz) sugar
- 50g (1¾oz) self-raising flour
- ½ tsp vanilla extract
- 3 eggs, whisked

For the icing

- 225g (8oz) icing sugar
- 2–3 tbsp water
- Food colouring

Makes 20

1. Preheat your oven to 180°C (350°F). Line your baking trays with cupcake cases. You'll need enough for 20 cupcakes.

2. Mix the butter and sugar together until creamy. Add the flour, vanilla, and eggs. Stir until everything is fully mixed together.

3. Spoon the mixture into the cupcake cases and place the trays in the oven. Bake for 15 minutes or until they are firm and golden.

4. Leave the cupcakes to cool. For flat-topped cupcakes, slice off the tops. Mix the icing ingredients together and decorate your cupcakes.

Baking bread

2½ hours

There's nothing quite like the smell of freshly baked bread – and it's easier to make than you'd think. You can also use this dough to make other bready things, including rolls and pizza.

Ingredients
- 1½ tsp dried yeast
- 1 tsp caster sugar
- 350ml (12fl oz) warm water
- 500g (1lb, 2oz) strong white bread flour
- 2 tsp of salt • 1 tbsp olive oil
- 1 egg, beaten

1. Mix the yeast and sugar with half of the warm water. Leave it in a warm place for about 10 minutes, or until it starts to bubble.

2. Sieve the flour and salt into a bowl and make a well in the centre. Pour in the yeast mixture, the oil, and the remaining water, and mix well.

3. Put a little flour on your hands and the work surface, and knead the dough for 10 minutes, until it's smooth.

4. Place the dough in a large bowl and cover it with clingfilm. Put it in a warm (not hot) place for an hour, or until it has doubled in size.

5. Preheat the oven to 220°C (425°F). Push your fist into the dough to knock some of the air out of it. Then knead it for another 5 minutes.

6. Put the dough in a greased loaf tin. Leave it in a warm place for another 10 minutes to rise. Brush it with the egg, then bake for 30 mins.

Making rolls

Instead of putting the dough in the loaf tin, divide it into small balls. Flatten them slightly and leave to rise for 30 minutes. Top with milk and seeds, then bake for 25 minutes.

Pizza toppings

The great thing about pizza is that by changing the toppings you can make them taste really different. See which ones you like best.

Ham and pineapple

Ingredients

- 2-3 tbsp tomato purée or passata
- 3 slices of ham, cut into strips
- A few pineapple chunks, sliced
- Mozzarella cheese, torn

1. Buy premade pizza dough and roll it out into discs 18cm (7in) across.

Pepperoni and pepper

Ingredients

- 2-3 tbsp tomato purée or passata
- Pepperoni slices
- Half a yellow pepper, sliced
- Mozzarella cheese, torn

2. Preheat the oven to 220°C (425°F). Spread over the tomato puree or passata. Add your toppings, then bake for 20 minutes, until golden.

Serves 4

64

Tomato and olives

Ingredients

• 2-3 tbsp tomato purée
  or passata
• 3 tomatoes, sliced
• Black olives, sliced
• Fresh basil leaves

Cheese-free
pizza is
delicious too!

Ingredients

• 2-3 tbsp tomato purée
  or passata
• 125g (4½oz)
  mushrooms, sliced
• Mozzarella cheese, torn

Mushroom and mozzarella

Other toppings

Here are other toppings
you can use. Try several
at once.

• Sausage (cooked)
• Chicken (cooked)
• Onions
• Jalapeño peppers
• Bacon (cooked)
• Meatballs (cooked)
• Avocado
• Spinach
• Egg

If you're making recipes
that you aren't sure you'll
like, divide the pizza into
quarters and put different
toppings on each section.
That way, if you don't like
one, you haven't ruined a
whole pizza!

65

Dips and nibbles

Here are three great dips to share with your friends. And you can make them in a matter of minutes. Here's how.

Guacamole

Ingredients
- 3 ripe avocados
- ½ red onion, diced
- 1 garlic clove, crushed
- Juice of 1 lime • 2 tomatoes, deseeded and diced
- 3 tbsp chopped coriander

Good guacamole should have nice big chunks

1. Cut the avocados in half and remove the stones. Scoop out the flesh, chop it up, and put it in a bowl.

2. Add the rest of the ingredients and season with salt and pepper. Mash everything together and serve.

Hoummous

Ingredients

- 400g (14oz) chick-peas
- ½ tsp ground cumin
- 1 garlic clove, chopped
- 3 tbsp olive oil
- 2 tbsp tahini paste
- Juice of ½ lemon

1. Put all of the ingredients into a food processor and blend until smooth – easy!

If you like spice, sprinkle a little paprika on top

Salsa

Ingredients

- 350g (12oz) tomatoes
- ½ red onion, chopped
- Juice of ½ lime
- 4 tbsp coriander, chopped
- 2 garlic cloves, chopped
- 1 green chilli chopped

Melt a little cheese on tortillas. Sprinkle with sea salt and black pepper for a perfect dipping tool!

1. Cut the tomatoes in half, remove the seeds, and dice the flesh. Mix with all the other ingredients.

Gingerbread

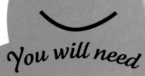

If you're in the mood for something a little less fiddly than a gingerbread house, you can always go back to basics and bake delicious gingerbread cookies. Don't forget to decorate them!

Makes 10

You will need
- 600g (1lb, 5oz) plain flour
- 2 tsp bicarbonate of soda
- 2 tbsp ginger
- 250g (9oz) unsalted butter, softened
- 150g (5½oz) brown sugar
- 2 eggs
- 100g (3½oz) treacle

1. Sift the flour, bicarbonate of soda and ginger into a mixing bowl.

2. Mix the butter and sugar in a second bowl until it's nice and smooth.

3. Add the eggs to the butter mix and beat together. Add the treacle slowly, stirring to mix well.

4. Add the flour mixture a few spoonfuls at a time, mixing it together as you go.

5. Flatten the dough and wrap it in clingfilm. Put it in the fridge for an hour so that it firms up.

6. Preheat the oven to 180°C (350°F). Roll the dough into a 3mm (⅛in) sheet and cut out shapes with a cookie cutter. Bake for 15 minutes.

Use coloured icing when decorating

Decoration

Use different shaped cookie cutters, such as angels, stars, and snowmen. Decorate the cookies with sweets and writing icing.

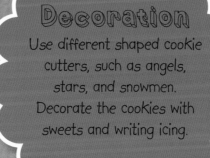

Folded napkins

Help set the table with these funky folded napkins. Not only are they quick to make, but you can use them to hold cutlery, as place settings, or to hold other napkins. Perfect for a birthday meal!

You will need

- Coloured paper napkins
- Glitter and gems
- Craft glue

1. Unfold two different coloured napkins and place one on top of the other. Fold them in half twice.

2. Take the top loose corner of the first napkin and fold underneath to make a pocket.

3. Repeat with the other layers, leaving a 1cm (½in) strip between each fold.

4. Turn the napkins over and fold the two side corners into the centre to create a cone shape.

5. Decorate with gems, glitters, and sparkles. Open the pocket to place your cutlery inside.

Colour coordinate these napkins with place settings

Drink stirrers

If you're making people drinks, put one of these drink mixers into their glasses. It will make the drinks look nice, and they can be used to stir the drinks. If you wash them properly you can reuse them too!

1. Cut two identical butterfly shapes out of coloured card. Bend the wings back and glue them to the top part of the straw.

2. Decorate the butterflies with gems and stickers. Then make some more mixers with different shapes such as stars or flowers.

Try creating other folded napkins like these ones. Or if you're feeling creative, try to come up with your very own styles.

Handmade cards

The next time someone you know has a birthday, instead of buying them a card, why not make your own? You can make it look exactly how you want and they'll really appreciate the effort you've made.

You will need
- Coloured paper
- Scissors
- Glue

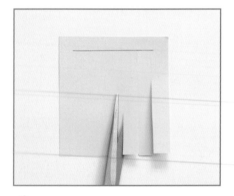

1. Draw a pencil line on a square piece of paper 2.5cm (1in) from the top. Cut strips every 2.5cm (1in) along the bottom, towards the line.

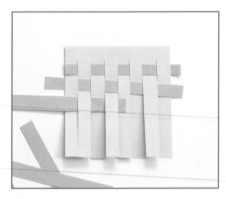

2. Cut 2.5cm (1in) wide strips out of a different coloured piece of paper. Thread them over and under the strips, making a weave.

3. Keep doing this until you've got a chequered pattern. Glue the flaps at the edge to keep them secure.

4. Fold a larger piece of paper in half twice and then unfold it so it looks like this. Cut out a shape in the bottom right corner.

5. Glue your chequered pattern to the opposite side from where you cut out your shape so that it shows through.

6. Fold the paper again to make a square. Now all you need to do is write your message on the inside.

Origami heart

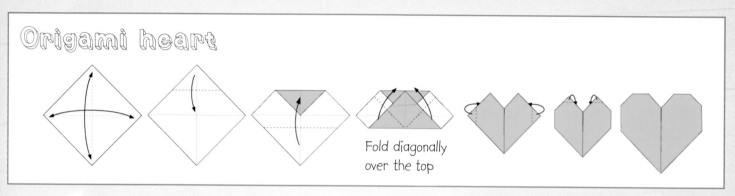

Fold diagonally over the top

Make origami hearts and glue them on to give your cards a cool 3-D effect

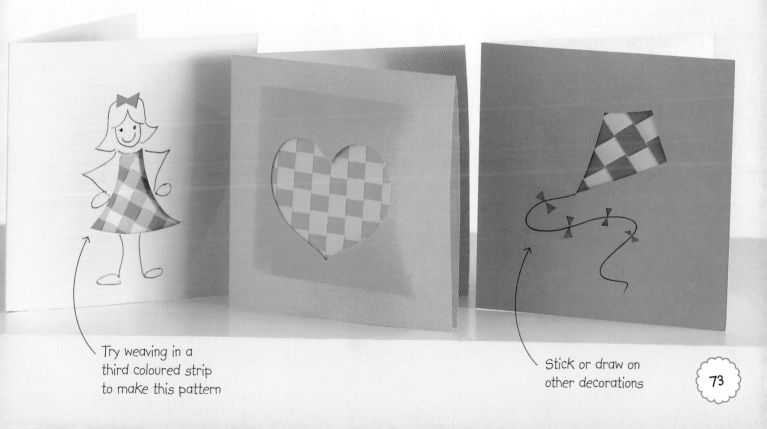

Try weaving in a third coloured strip to make this pattern

Stick or draw on other decorations

Party invitations

The next time you're having a party, why not make your own invitations and place settings. It will look great, and everybody will be impressed by your creativity.

You will need

- White and pink card
- Glue
- Coloured paper
- Felt shapes, sequins, ribbons, and glitter
- Envelopes

1. Fold the white card in half. Cut the pink card to the same size and draw a 2.5cm (1in) border around it. Cut it out to make a frame.

2. Stick the frame to the front of the white card. While the glue dries, cut out balloon and present shapes from the coloured paper.

3. Decorate the frame with felt shapes, sequins, gems, and ribbon. Glue your paper decorations to the white card and add glitter.

4. Wrap ribbon around the envelopes, and glue on more sequins. Don't forget to write in the cards before you seal them!

Place settings

Divide a piece of card into three equal sections and cut off any excess. Fold your card into a triangle shape so that one middle section acts as a base. Secure the triangle with tape. Cut out a heart shape from the coloured paper and glue it to the front of the card. Decorate with sequins, ribbons, and glitter, then write your friends' names on the front.

You will need
• Coloured card
• Tape • Coloured paper
• Glue • Sequins, ribbons, and glitter

Gift boxes

Fabulous wrapping and packaging can really make a difference when you're giving gifts. Fill these beautiful boxes with scrumptious treats and give them to somebody to make their day.

You will need
- Plain boxes
- Paintbrush and paints
- Coloured paper or felt
- Glue • Glitter and beads
- Ribbons
- Tissue paper

Filling
You can fill your boxes with anything you think your friends will like. Toffee and chocolates are great, or you could use the boxes for jewellery.

Try to make each box look different

1. Paint the outside of your boxes and leave to dry. Cut out flowers and stars from paper or felt, and glue them to the lids.

2. Decorate the boxes with glitter and beads, and wrap ribbon around the outside. Line the inside of each box with tissue paper.

Ribbon, lace, and flowers look great as decorations

Use round, square, or heart-shaped boxes

77

Birthday cake

No birthday is complete without a great big delicious cake. This recipe will be loved by grown-ups too!

Ingredients

- 175g (6oz) butter (softened)
- 175g (6oz) brown sugar
- 150g (5½oz) self-raising flour
- 25g (1oz) cocoa powder
- ½ tsp bicarbonate of soda
- 3 eggs (beaten)
- 100ml (3½fl oz) sour cream

For the icing

- 125g (4½oz) butter
- 175g (6oz) chocolate
- 4 tbsp milk
- 200g (7oz) icing sugar

1. Preheat the oven to 170°C (375°F). Line 2 x 20cm (8in) cake tins with baking paper.

2. Whisk the butter and sugar in a bowl. Add the flour, cocoa powder, bicarbonate of soda, eggs, and sour cream. Mix together until smooth.

3. Divide the mixture evenly between the cake tins and smooth the tops. Bake the cakes for about 25-30 minutes, until the top feels springy.

4. Turn out the cakes onto a cooling rack. Remove the baking paper. While they cool, it's time to make the icing.

5. Put the butter, chocolate, and milk in a bowl over a pan of simmering water. When the mixture has melted, stir in the icing sugar.

6. Once the icing has cooled, spread it on one sponge, then place the other on top. Spread the rest on top and around the sides.

Decoration

Your cake will look and taste even better if you decorate it with sweets. Try to mix things that have bright colours and different shapes. Don't forget the candles either!

Add chocolate shavings and mini balls for a grown-up version

Try not to eat it all at once!

These bags will make a perfect gift

Put your scented bags in a drawer with your clothes to make them smell lovely

Filling
Fill your bags with dried lavender or pot pourri and tie ribbon around the top of the bag to close it up.

Scented bags

If you're having a clear out, don't just throw away your old clothes – recycle them! You won't believe how easy it is to turn an old jumper into a pretty scented bag to go in your drawers.

1. Cut off a large piece of the jumper and lay it flat. If you want to use the sleeves, cut them off and turn them inside out.

2. Pin the paper template to the fabric and cut around it to make two rectangles. Put the pieces on top of each other and pin together.

3. Sew around the edges of your rectangles, leaving 1cm (½in) around the edge. Leave one edge unsewn, and turn the bag inside out..

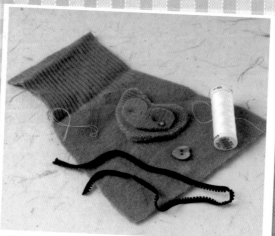

4. Cut small hearts or other shapes from any spare fabric and sew them to the front of your bags. Sew on buttons to decorate.

Glove purses

It's easy to turn an old pair of gloves or mittens
into a funky purse for your coins or buttons.
Why not make them for your friends too?

You will need
- Old gloves
- Needle and thread
- Sewing pins
- Zips
- Buttons and beads
- Scraps of felt, wool, and ribbon

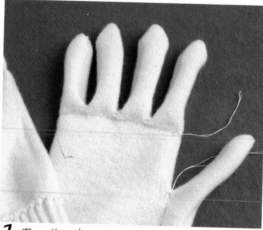

1. Turn the gloves inside out and sew along the bottom of the fingers. This will pin the two sides of the glove together to stop anything falling out.

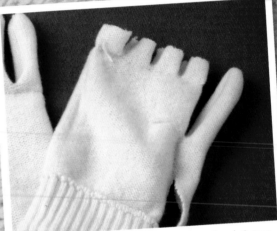

2. Cut off the fingers and thumbs about 0.5cm (¼in) away from the seam you made. Pin and sew a zip into the cuff end.

3. Using a zip that is the same length as the cuff, pin and sew the zip into the cuff end.

4. Use buttons, beads, felt, wool, and ribbon to decorate your purses. Make them look like people or animals.

Theme your purses

If you're planning to make a few purses, pick a theme and try to make them match. If they're going to be Christmas presents, for example, you could try to make a snowman, reindeer, or Santa purse.

Felt decorations

You can make these to pretty decorations to sew on a bag or cushion or hang them in your room. Use whatever scraps of felt you have handy.

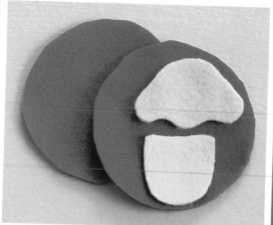

1. Decide what you're going to make and cut the shapes out from different coloured felt. This design is a pretty cupcake

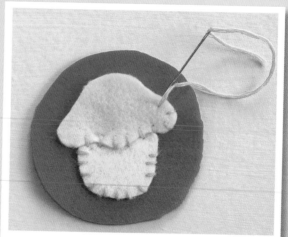

2. Use the needle and thread to sew the pieces to a background. Use a different colour thread to your fabric.

3. Glue or stitch beads, sequins, or buttons to add detail to your design.

4. Stitch your design to another piece of felt and stuff wadding between them. Add a ribbon to make a hanger, and sew the edges to finish.

You can make birds, hearts, and flowers

Attach beads and sequins as decorations

Beaded insects

Hang butterflies and dragonflies from your blinds or curtains, or in your windows where they can sparkle in the light. They will also make lovely necklaces as gifts for your friends.

1. Unspool about 30cm (12in) of craft wire. Thread a few black beads and then a white one onto the wire to make the body.

2. Take the end of the craft wire back down through the top three beads and out of the side. Leave a small loop at the top.

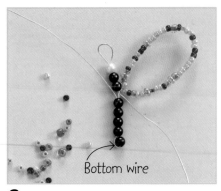

3. Push the wire at the bottom back through the beads and out of the left side. Thread beads onto the wire on the right to make a wing.

Bottom wire

4. Twist the wing so that it stays in place. Repeat this for the bottom wing to complete the first side.

5. Do the same thing on the other side of the butterfly. Try to bend all four wings so they look as similar as possible.

6. Twist the wires around the body a few times to keep the beads in place. If you have any excess wire, trim it off with scissors.

Thread ribbon through the loop to make pendants

Squish the wings long to make dragonfly wings

Magic flowers

You will need
- A white flower with a long stem
- 2 glasses or vases
- Tape
- Food colouring

Did you know you can change the colour of a flower? Try this experiment and see for yourself: it's like magic!

1. Lay your flower on a chopping board. Ask an adult to cut the stem lengthways up to about the halfway point.

2. Wrap a piece of tape around where the cut was made to stop the stem from splitting any further.

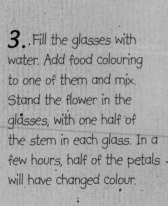

3. Fill the glasses with water. Add food colouring to one of them and mix. Stand the flower in the glasses, with one half of the stem in each glass. In a few hours, half of the petals will have changed colour.

Carnations and large daisies work very well for this

Xylem

How this works

Plants draw water from the soil through their roots. It travels up the stem through a hollow tube – called the xylem. In this case, as the water is drawn up from the glass, the food colouring travels with it, dying the petal once it reaches the top.

Because the stem is cut in half, the food colouring only travels up half of the xylem, which is why the whole flower doesn't change colour

Horoscopes

Some people believe that the date of your birth affects your personality, and that you can predict the future by observing the stars. This is called astrology.

Pisces
19 Feb – 20 Mar
(The Fishes)

Aries
21 Mar – 19 Apr
(The Ram)

Aquarius
20 Jan – 18 Feb
(The Water Bearer)

Taurus
20 Apr – 20 May
(The Bull)

Capricorn
22 Dec – 19 Jan
(The Goat)

Gemini
21 May – 20 Jun
(The Twins)

There are 12 different star signs. This is because the Sun passes through 12 constellations in a year. Astrologers split these signs into four groups that share similar traits: earth, fire, air, and water. But each sign has its own unique traits and its own symbol (usually an animal).

Cancer
21 Jun – 22 Jul
(The Crab)

Sagittarius
22 Nov – 21 Dec
(The Archer)

Leo
23 Jul – 22 Aug
(The Lion)

Scorpio
23 Oct – 21 Nov
(The Scorpion)

Libra
23 Sept – 22 Oct
(The Scales)

Virgo
23 Aug – 22 Sept
(The Maiden)

Earth signs

Politeness and sociability are said to be among the traits of those born under earth signs.

Taurus: Dependable, clever, sporty
Virgo: Creative, intelligent, helpful
Capricorn: Wise, disciplined, calm

Air signs

Being born under an air sign is supposed to make a person curious and good at communicating.

Aquarius: Creative, inventive, friendly
Gemini: Sociable, energetic, childlike
Libra: Kind, artistic, sociable

Water signs

People born under a water sign are generally quite sensitive, and are good at reading people.

Pisces: Dreamy, popular, artistic
Cancer: Gentle, caring, nurturing
Scorpio: Passionate, focused, intense

Are they accurate?

Now you know the traits of all the star signs, why not put them to the test? Get together with your friends and ask them what their star signs are. Does their personality match the descriptions?

Fire signs

Anybody born under a fire sign is thought to be bright and strong, but can also be reckless.

Aries: Independent, energetic, intelligent
Leo: Ambitious, active, confident
Sagittarius: Lively, adventurous, optimistic

Chinese horoscopes

Chinese astrology works differently. Again, there are 12 different signs, but each one is based on the year you were born. So anybody born in 2013 would be born in the "Year of the Snake".

Glossary

Acrylic paints
A fast-drying, water-based paint that is often used in arts and crafts.

All-purpose glue
A type of glue suitable for use on many different surfaces, such as wood, glass, metal and textiles.

Bicarbonate of soda
A chemical that is used in baking to make bread and cakes rise.

Blender
A kitchen appliance with a rotating blade that is used to puree and mix foods.

Bondaweb
A material used to hem garments, as an alternative to hand-stitching.

Cork
A material harvested from bark, often used as flooring or as bottle stoppers.

Corn oil
Oil extracted from maize, commonly used for frying.

Craft wire
Metal wire used in crafts. It is generally easy to bend. It can be made from a variety of metals, such as copper, brass, silver and gold.

Dulce de leche
A sweet toffee-like substance popular in South America, made by slowly heating sweetened milk.

Embroidery thread
A fine yarn made specifically for embroidery.

Emulsion paint
A quick-drying, versatile paint frequently used on large areas such as walls and ceilings, and can also be used on wooden furniture.

Glue gun
An appliance for heating and applying glue at high temperatures. It is frequently used on hard materials such as plastic and wood.

Petroleum jelly
A colourless, translucent ointment that is frequently used on chapped lips and skin.

Pinboard
A surface used to hold pieces of paper such as letters, postcards, and photographs. They are often made of cork and the messages are secured to them with pins, to make it easier to add and remove items.

Polythene bags
A type of plastic bag used for carrying shopping.

Popping corn
A type of corn which expands and puffs up when heated to make popcorn.

Sandpaper
A heavy material with an abrasive surface used to remove material from surfaces, often to make them smoother.

Satinwood paint
A paint designed for use on interior wood, which has a slightly glossy surface that can be wiped clean.

Soil-based compost
Compost consists of decomposed organic material mixed with soil, and is frequently used in gardening to aid plant growth.

Sour cream
A cream with a mildly sour taste. It is frequently used in salad dressing, baking, and South American cuisine.

Staple gun
A hand-held device that is used to drive staples into paper, wood, plastic and masonry. Unlike the stapler found in an office, it does not need to be placed on either side of the material that is being stapled.

Suede twine
Narrow laces of thin, soft leather.

Tomato puree/passata
Tomatoes mashed or chopped to a fine consistency, often used on pizza.

Turpentine
A liquid solvent often used to thin oil-based paint, obtained by distilling tree resin.

Undercoat paint
Paint applied to mask imperfections in the surface and to protect the top coat from chips and scrapes.

Vanilla
A flavouring taken from the Vanilla orchid, widely used in baking and perfumery.

Wadding
A layer of material, normally cotton, polyester or wool, used to provide insulation or padding in crafts such as quilting.

Whisk
A utensil used to blend ingredients during cooking.

Witch hazel
A substance extracted from the witch hazel plant, commonly used on skin blemishes and bruising.

Index

DK would like to thank

Becky Alexander and Carrie Love for proofreading, Sarah Isle for production assistance, Margaret Parrish for Americanization, Sonia Charbonnier for technical assistance, and Romaine Werblow for image sourcing.